P9-AZV-662

IT'S A
MAGICAL
WORLD

Other Books by Bill Watterson

Calvin and Hobbes
Something Under the Bed Is Drooling
Yukon Ho!
Weirdos from Another Planet
The Revenge of the Baby-Sat
Scientific Progress Goes "Boink"
Attack of the Deranged Mutant Killer Monster Snow Goons
The Days Are Just Packed
Homicidal Psycho Jungle Cat
There's Treasure Everywhere

Treasury Collections

The Essential Calvin and Hobbes
The Calvin and Hobbes Lazy Sunday Book
The Authoritative Calvin and Hobbes
The Indispensable Calvin and Hobbes
The Calvin and Hobbes Tenth Anniversary Book

IT'S A MAGICAL WORLD

WORLD

A Calvin and Hobbes Collection by Bill Watterson

SCHOLASTIC INC.
New York Toronto London Auckland Sydney

Calvin and Hobbes is distributed internationally by Universal Press Syndicate.

No part of this publication may be reproduced in whole or in part, or stored in a retrieval system, or transmitted in any form or by any means, electronic, mechanical, photocopying, recording, or otherwise, without written permission of the publisher. For information regarding permission, write to Andrews and McMeel, a Universal Press Syndicate Company, 4520 Main Street, Kansas City, MO 64111.

ISBN 0-590-97207-3

Copyright © 1996 by Bill Watterson.
All rights reserved. Published by Scholastic Inc., 555 Broadway, New York, NY 10012, by arrangement with Andrews and McMeel, a Universal Press Syndicate Company.

12 11 10 9 8 7 6 5 4 3 2 1   7 8 9/9 0 1 2/0

Printed in the U.S.A.   14

First Scholastic printing, January 1997

calvin and Hobbes by WATTERSON

5

WOULD YOU CARE FOR A SNACK, SUSIE?

UM, OK. THANK YOU.

WELL? WHAT HAVE YOU GOT TO SAY FOR YOURSELF?

WHEN ONE ENTERTAINS FEMALE FRIENDS, ONE SHOULD TRY NOT TO LOOK QUITE AS SEEDY AS CERTAIN UNNAMED PARTIES HABITUALLY DO.

WHO'S ENTERTAINING?! WHO'S A FEMALE FRIEND? WHO LOOKS SEEDY?!

A SPOTTED TIE IS JUST THE THING WHEN YOU'RE WEARING STRIPES! TIGERS HAVE A NATURAL FLAIR FOR CASUAL CHIC!

I CAN'T BELIEVE THIS! WHY DIDN'T YOU KILL HER WHEN SHE CAME IN THE DOOR?!

BY THE WAY, IF YOU HAD MADE PROPER INTRODUCTIONS, WE MIGHT HAVE SMOOCHED HER HAND.

HERE, LET ME ADJUST THE NARROW END OF YOUR TIE ABOUT EIGHT INCHES.

WHAT HAPPENED TO *YOU*?

HOBBES AND I HAD A FRANK EXCHANGE OF IDEAS.

WHAT ARE YOU DOING? HOMEWORK??

I WASN'T SURE I UNDERSTOOD THIS CHAPTER, SO I REVIEWED MY NOTES FROM THE LAST CHAPTER AND NOW I'M REREADING THIS.

YOU DO ALL THAT *WORK*?!

WELL, NOW I UNDERSTAND IT.

HUH! I USED TO THINK YOU WERE SMART.

CaLViN and HObbEs
by WATTERSON

THE SECRET TO ENJOYING YOUR JOB IS TO HAVE A HOBBY THAT'S EVEN WORSE.

What was the significance of the Erie Canal?

IN tHE COSMIC SENSE, PRObably NiL.

WE "BIG PICTURE" PEOPLE RARELY BECOME HISTORIANS.

REMEMBER WHEN I WAS FIRST BORN? I COULDN'T EVEN TURN MYSELF OVER! MY EYES WOULDN'T FOCUS! I COULDN'T DO ANYTHING!

THINK OF ALL THE WORK IT TOOK TO DEVELOP THE MOTOR SKILLS NECESSARY TO HOLD A CRAYON, TO PLACE THE TIP OF IT ON A PAGE, AND TO MOVE IT IN PREDETERMINED, COORDINATED MOTIONS!

THIS PICTURE IS THE RESULT OF SIX YEARS' UNRELENTING TOIL! A LIFETIME OF EFFORT WENT INTO THIS!

I'M STILL NOT PAYING YOU $500 FOR IT.

IT WILL APPRECIATE! IT'S AN INVESTMENT!

AH, WHAT A LOVELY DAY TO GO SAILING, EH MARSHA?

OUR NEW BOAT IS JUST WONDERFUL, BRADLEY.

WHAT DO YOU SAY WE DROP ANCHOR AND GO FOR A SWIM, DEAREST?

THAT SOUNDS DELIGHTFUL, DARLING! LET'S GO!

PLOOSH PLOOSH

AAA!! AAA!!

THIS LAKE IS BOILING HOT! WE'RE GETTING SCALDED!! GET OUT OF THE WATER! AA! OW! AA! OW!

I'VE GOT SECOND DEGREE BURNS ALL OVER! WHAT KIND OF LAKE *IS* THIS ?!

WE NEED MEDICAL ATTENTION, BRADLEY! PULL UP THE ANCHOR!

BRADLEY, WE'RE GOING THE WRONG WAY!

I CAN'T HELP IT, MARSHA! THE WIND IS BLOWING US OVER HERE, TOWARD THE... THE...

THE WATERFALL! OH NO! AAAAA! BLUB BLUB! AAAA! GLUB GLUB GLUB!

HELP, HELP! THE WIND IS PICKING UP AGAIN! HANG ON! WE'RE FLYING RIGHT OUT OF THE WATER!

DON'T LOOK DOWN, MARSHA! WE'RE MILES HIGH!

UH OH! THE WIND SUDDENLY STOPPED!!

AAAAA A AAAA A AAAAAA A

WE..WE'RE ALIVE! WE SOMEHOW LANDED IN ANOTHER LAKE! BUT WHERE *ARE* WE ??

I HAVE A BAD FEELING ABOUT THIS, BRADLEY.

IT'S A GIGANTIC WHIRLPOOL!! WE'RE GOING DOWN! WAAAAAAA!!

HERE'S THE PROBLEM. THAT'LL BE $150.

SOMEBODY *ELSE* IS GOING TO PAY FOR THIS TOO.

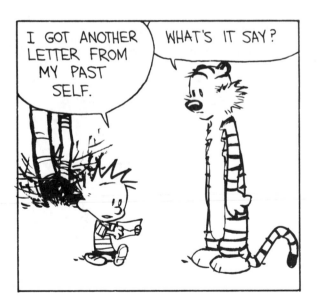

CALVIN and HOBBES by WATTERSON

THIS NEW ISSUE OF *CHEWING* MAGAZINE TELLS HOW TO SET UP A MANDIBULAR FITNESS REGIME!

BASICALLY, THEY RECOMMEND INTERVAL TRAINING: CHEWING ONE PIECE OF GUM WITH LOTS OF REPS, FOLLOWED BY CHEWING FIVE PIECES OF GUM AT ONCE, SO YOU REALLY WORK THE MASSETER AND BUCCINATOR MUSCLES.

IT'S A GRUELING WORKOUT, BUT YOU BUILD STRENGTH **AND** ENDURANCE, SO YOU CAN COME THROUGH IN A CLINCHER.

I'M SURE THE GLORY MAKES IT ALL WORTHWHILE.

PLUS, YOU DEVELOP THAT "CHEWER'S JAW" THAT DRIVES THE GIRLS WILD.

WHAT'S WITH THE FACE?

I'M DOING STRETCHES.

CHEWING MAGAZINE SAYS YOU SHOULD ALWAYS WARM UP BEFORE YOU CHEW GUM.

DID YOU KNOW THAT NEGLECTING TO STRETCH THE TEMPORALIS MUSCLES IS THE LEADING CAUSE OF GUM CHEWING INJURIES?

WHAT ABOUT FALLING DOWN WHILE CHEWING AND WALKING?

WITH A GOOD HELMET, THE RISK IS SURPRISINGLY SMALL.

IN THIS ISSUE, *CHEWING* REVIEWS THE NEW GUM CHEWING APPAREL.

THIS JERSEY IS MADE WITH SWET-TEK® FIBERS THAT WICK AWAY PERSPIRATION! THE MESH COLLAR KEEPS YOUR STERNOMASTOIDS VENTILATED AND THE ZIPPERED POCKETS HOLD SPARE GUM AND WRAPPERS!

WHY IS IT COVERED WITH BRAND LOGOS?

THAT GIVES YOU THE PSYCHOLOGICAL EDGE OF PRETENDING YOU'RE SPONSORED.

HOW CAN YOU TELL IF YOU'RE READING AN ADVERTISEMENT, A PRODUCT REVIEW, OR THE PRODUCT ITSELF?

I'D SURE LIKE TO BE A WALKING ENDORSEMENT.

I NEED TO GET A HEART RATE MONITOR.

WHAT FOR?

TO MAKE SURE I'M CHEWING AT MY AEROBIC THRESHOLD! EVERY DAY I WANT TO SEE THAT I'M CHEWING MORE GUM FASTER, HARDER, AND LONGER!

WHAT'S THE POINT OF ATTACHING A NUMBER TO EVERYTHING YOU DO?

IF YOUR NUMBERS GO UP, IT MEANS YOU'RE HAVING MORE FUN.

SCIENCE TO THE SPIRIT'S RESCUE ONCE AGAIN.

I HATE WHEN A LOT OF KIDS ARE ON THE SLIDE. YOU WAIT FOREVER TO GET TO THE TOP AND THEN THE RIDE IS OVER SO FAST.

AND IF YOU SIT FOR A MOMENT TO ENJOY THE HEIGHT, EVERYBODY YELLS AT YOU TO GET GOING.

AND SOMETIMES THE IDIOT BEHIND YOU STARTS DOWN TOO SOON AND HE SMACKS INTO YOU AT THE BOTTOM BEFORE YOU CAN GET AWAY.

YEP, THE PLAYGROUND IS A *LOT* MORE FUN AFTER CLASS STARTS.

CALVIN!

PHOOMPP

WHY ARE YOU CRYING?

I'M CUTTING UP AN ONION.

IT MUST BE HARD TO COOK IF YOU ANTHROPOMORPHIZE YOUR VEGETABLES.

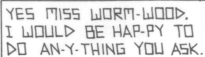

28

calvin and hobbes
by watterson

Calvin and Hobbes
by WATTERSON

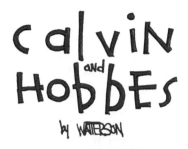

YOU KNOW, HOBBES, SOME DAYS EVEN MY LUCKY ROCKETSHIP UNDERPANTS DON'T HELP.

WELL, YOU'VE DONE ALL YOU CAN DO.

34

PHOOOOFF

 WOW! LOOK AT THE SIZE OF THAT ONE!

BIP

 SECRETLY, I WAS HOPING FOR A DEAFENING EXPLOSION.

FFOOOOFF

FFOOOOF

BIP

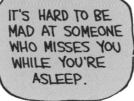

AACKKK

CH...CH...CH...

..CHOCOLATE CH-CHIPS..

NO.

AND GET UP OFF THE FLOOR.

URGLE

I'M A GREAT BELIEVER IN THE VALUE OF NOVELTY.

I SAY ANYTHING NEW IS GOOD BY DEFINITION! IT CAN SHOCK, INSULT, OR OFFEND ME, SO LONG AS IT DOESN'T BORE ME!

IF YOU CAN'T GIVE ME SOMETHING NEW, THEN REPACKAGE THE OLD SO IT LOOKS NEW! NOVELTY IS ALL THAT MATTERS! I WON'T PAY ATTENTION IF IT'S NOT FRESH AND DIFFERENT!

I SEE WHY TIMELESS TRUTH DOESN'T SELL.

GIVE ME A GOOD FLASH IN THE PAN ANY DAY.

YAWWNN

YAWNNN

YYAWNN   YAWWNN

ONE OF US SHOULD HAVE LEFT THE ROOM.

Z

WHEN I WAS A KID, MY MOM WOULD TAKE ME TO THE BIG OLD DEPARTMENT STORE DOWNTOWN, AND I USED TO LOVE RIDING THE ESCALATORS.

THE ESCALATORS THERE HAD WOOD STAIRS, AND THEY USED TO CLICK, CLACK, AND CREAK. THE WOOD SLATS ON EACH STEP WERE MAYBE HALF AN INCH APART, AND I ALWAYS WONDERED IF LADIES GOT THEIR HIGH HEELS STUCK AND GOT PULLED UNDER.

SOME OF THOSE ESCALATORS WERE VERY NARROW—JUST WIDE ENOUGH FOR ONE PERSON. YEP, THOSE OLD ESCALATORS HAD A LOT MORE PERSONALITY THAN THESE SLICK METAL ONES.

I'D HATE TO THINK THAT ALL MY CURRENT EXPERIENCES WILL SOMEDAY BECOME STORIES WITH NO POINT.

41

THINGS I WILL NEVER LIKE:

1. DRYING OFF WITH A COLD, damp TOWEL.
2. THE FEELING OF SEAWEED WRAPPING AROUND MY LEG.

3. ANYTHING THAT WAS POPULAR IN THE '70s.
4. LICORICE, YAMS, OR RAISINS.
5. THAT HIGH-PITCHED SCREECH THAT BABIES MAKE.
6. WRITHING MAGGOTS.

IT'S COMFORTING TO KNOW THAT THERE ARE CERTAINTIES IN LIFE.

LIFE IS FULL OF POSSIBILITIES.

FOR EXAMPLE, RIGHT NOW, INSTEAD OF WAITING FOR THE SCHOOL BUS, I COULD STICK OUT MY THUMB, HITCH A RIDE, AND SPEND THE REST OF MY LIFE IN THE SERENGETI, MIGRATING WITH THE WILDEBEESTS!

THE SERENGETI IS IN AFRICA. YOU COULDN'T REALLY HITCH A RIDE THERE.

LIFE IS FULL OF PRECLUDED POSSIBILITIES.

calvin and Hobbes _{by WATTERSON}

THE FEARLESS SPACEMAN SPIFF, INTERPLANETARY EXPLORER EXTRAORDINAIRE, GAZES ACROSS THE FORBIDDING LANDSCAPE OF AN UNCHARTED PLANET!

WHAT DANGERS LIE AHEAD FOR OUR HERO? WHAT HORRIBLE ALIENS INHABIT THIS WORLD?

WHAT STRANGE ADVENTURES AWAIT THE INTREPID SPIFF? WHAT BIZARRE OCCURRENCE WILL OUR HERO BE THE FIRST TO WITNESS?

THE SUSPENSE!

...OUR HERO CHUCKS A FEW ROCKS...

...SIGHHH...

IF YOU COULDN'T FIND ANY WEIRDNESS, MAYBE WE'LL JUST HAVE TO MAKE SOME!

NOW YER TALKIN'!

OUCHYWAWA.

WHEN YOUR AILMENTS SOUND CUTE, YOU DON'T GET MUCH SYMPATHY.

47

THINK ABOUT THE PLACES YOU CAN GO ONCE YOU LEARN HOW TO RIDE!

AAAA A

THINK ABOUT HOW IMPRESSED YOUR FRIENDS WILL BE! THINK ABOUT HOW MUCH FUN YOU'LL HAVE!

AAAA AAA

AAA A AAAA AA

THINK ABOUT INHALING.

..EEEP AHHH..

OOH, IT DOESN'T LOOK LIKE THE BIKE LESSON WENT SO GOOD.

IT DIDN'T.

DAD LIKES RIDING HIS BIKE! HE DOESN'T UNDERSTAND WHAT IT'S LIKE FOR ME!

I HATE FLIPPING OVER THE BARS, GETTING CHASED AROUND THE YARD, AND GETTING MOWED DOWN BY A DEMONIC MACHINE!

IS THAT WHAT HAPPENED?

NO, I TRIPPED COMING UP THE STAIRS.

calvin and Hobbes by WATTERSON

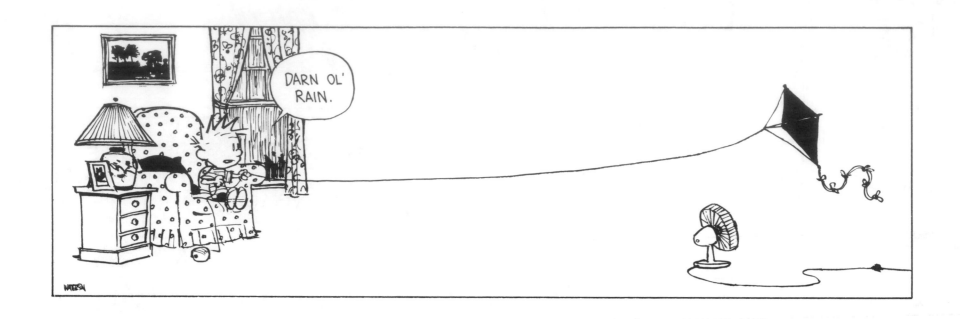

LOOK AT THIS! MOM GOT ME A BOOK FROM THE LIBRARY.

THAT'S NICE.

NICE?!? IT'S SUMMER! I ONLY GET THREE SHORT MONTHS TO GOOF OFF! I'M NOT GOING TO WASTE THESE PRECIOUS DAYS READING BOOKS!

SUMMERS ARE FOR VEGETATING! THAT'S WHY THE TV SHOWS ARE RERUNS AND THE MOVIES ARE SEQUELS!

NO WONDER THE FLIES COME OUT.

HECK, EVERYONE KNOWS IT'S NOT ENTERTAINMENT UNLESS YOU CAN SIT IN THE DARK AND EAT.

HEY, ARE YOU READING THAT BOOK MOM GOT ME FROM THE LIBRARY?

MM-HMM.

IS IT GOOD? DO YOU LIKE IT? IS IT EXCITING? ARE YOU HAVING FUN?

SHH.

HOW COULD IT POSSIBLY BE FUN WHEN IT'S SO QUIET?!?

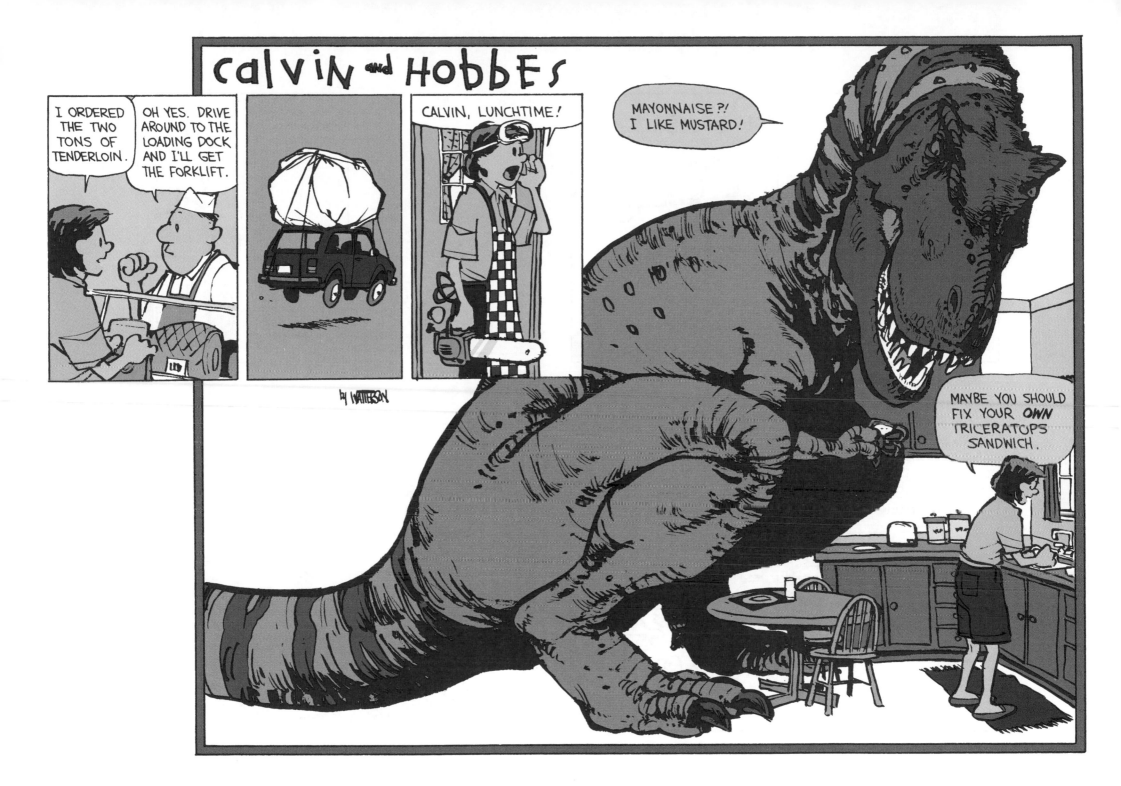

TIMES ARE TOUGH FOR US SUBURBAN POST-MODERNISTS.

HOW SO?

WELL, PEOPLE SEEM TO BE RELUCTANT TO PAY FOR SIDEWALK DRAWINGS THAT STAY WHERE THEY ARE AND WASH AWAY IN THE RAIN.

AND NOWADAYS, NOBODY WANTS TAX MONEY TO SUPPORT ART, AND CORPORATIONS WON'T UNDERWRITE ME BECAUSE I'M NOT FAMOUS ENOUGH TO EFFECTIVELY ADVERTISE THEIR CULTURAL ENLIGHTENMENT.

COULDN'T YOU SUPPORT YOUR ART WITH ANOTHER JOB?

WHAT, YOU MEAN *WORK*?

PEOPLE ALWAYS MAKE THE MISTAKE OF THINKING ART IS CREATED FOR THEM.

BUT REALLY, ART IS A PRIVATE LANGUAGE FOR SOPHISTICATES TO CONGRATULATE THEMSELVES ON THEIR SUPERIORITY TO THE REST OF THE WORLD.

AS MY ARTIST'S STATEMENT EXPLAINS, MY WORK IS UTTERLY INCOMPREHENSIBLE AND IS THEREFORE FULL OF DEEP SIGNIFICANCE.

YOU MISSPELLED "WELTANSCHAUUNG."

A GOOD ARTIST'S STATEMENT SAYS MORE THAN HIS ART EVER DOES.

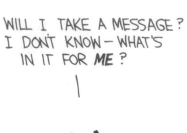

..H-HOTT...

SSSSSSS SSS

S SS SS S

SS SS SSS

AHHHH

..NOT AGAIN...

PEOPLE ASK WHY WE TOLERATE A POPULAR CULTURE THAT CELEBRATES VIOLENCE AND DEPRAVITY.

BECAUSE IT'S ENTERTAINING, THAT'S WHY!

IF WARPED VALUES ARE THE PRICE OF A VICARIOUS THRILL, SO BE IT! LET THE BUSINESS RESPOND TO CONSUMER DEMAND!

THE CUSTOMER IS ALWAYS RIGHT.

SHOCK AND TITILLATE ME! I'VE GOT MONEY!

POPULAR CULTURE ISN'T TO BLAME FOR SELLING TWISTED VALUES.

MOVIES, RECORDS, AND TV SHOWS REFLECT THE REALITY OF OUR TIMES. ARTISTS DEPICT HATRED AND VIOLENCE BECAUSE THAT'S WHAT THEY SEE.

WHY DON'T THEY SEE THINGS OF BEAUTY AND VALUE?

BECAUSE BORING STUFF DOESN'T SELL.

SUCH VISION AND INTEGRITY.

THERE'S NOTHING LIKE A GOOD GUNFIGHT TO UPLIFT THE SPIRIT.

ANOTHER THING TO REMEMBER ABOUT POPULAR CULTURE IS THAT TODAY'S TV-REARED AUDIENCE IS HIP AND SOPHISTICATED. THIS STUFF DOESN'T AFFECT US.

WE CAN SEPARATE FACT FROM FICTION. WE UNDERSTAND SATIRE AND IRONY. WE'RE DETACHED AND JADED VIEWERS WHO AREN'T INFLUENCED BY WHAT WE WATCH.

I THINK I HEAR ADVERTISERS LAUGHING.

HOLD ON, I NEED TO INFLATE MY BASKETBALL SHOES.

ONWARD CAME THE METEORS!

WE ALL WANT MEANINGFUL LIVES. WE LOOK FOR MEANING IN EVERYTHING WE DO.

BUT SUPPOSE THERE *IS* NO MEANING! SUPPOSE LIFE IS FUNDAMENTALLY ABSURD!

calviN and HobbES by WATTERSON

SUPPOSE THERE'S NO REASON, OR TRUTH, OR RIGHTNESS IN ANYTHING!

WHAT IF NOTHING MEANS ANYTHING? WHAT IF NOTHING REALLY MATTERS?

I GUESS THERE'S NO HARM IN A LITTLE WISHFUL THINKING.

OR SUPPOSE *EVERYTHING* MATTERS. WHICH WOULD BE WORSE??

77

 VAMPIRE BUGS! RUN FOR YOUR LIFE!

 THEY'RE CALLED MOSQUITOS.

 SO IF THEY DRINK YOUR BLOOD, YOU DON'T TURN INTO ONE?

 WHEN A PERSON PAUSES IN MID-SENTENCE TO CHOOSE A WORD, THAT'S THE BEST TIME TO JUMP IN AND CHANGE THE SUBJECT!

 IT'S LIKE AN INTERCEPTION IN FOOTBALL! YOU GRAB THE OTHER GUY'S IDEA AND RUN THE OPPOSITE WAY WITH IT!

 THE MORE SENTENCES YOU COMPLETE, THE HIGHER YOUR SCORE! THE IDEA IS TO BLOCK THE OTHER GUY'S THOUGHTS AND EXPRESS YOUR OWN! THAT'S HOW YOU WIN!

 CONVERSATIONS AREN'T CONTESTS! OK, A POINT FOR YOU, BUT I'M STILL AHEAD.

81

SOME PEOPLE ARE PRAGMATISTS, TAKING THINGS AS THEY COME AND MAKING THE BEST OF THE CHOICES AVAILABLE.

SOME PEOPLE ARE IDEALISTS, STANDING FOR PRINCIPLE AND REFUSING TO COMPROMISE.

AND SOME PEOPLE JUST ACT ON ANY WHIM THAT ENTERS THEIR HEADS.

I WONDER WHICH *YOU* ARE.

I PRAGMATICALLY TURN MY WHIMS INTO PRINCIPLES!

TO HELP MOM PREPARE BETTER MEALS, I'M COMPILING A BOOK OF RECIPES.

I NOTICE THAT ALL OF THEM INVOLVE DEEP-FAT FRYING.

I'M ADDING A CHOCOLATE SYRUP SECTION NOW.

IT USED TO BE THAT IF A CLIENT WANTED SOMETHING DONE IN A WEEK, IT WAS CONSIDERED A RUSH JOB, AND HE'D BE LUCKY TO GET IT.

NOW, WITH MODEMS, FAXES, AND CAR PHONES, EVERYBODY WANTS EVERYTHING INSTANTLY! IMPROVED TECHNOLOGY JUST INCREASES EXPECTATIONS.

THESE MACHINES DON'T MAKE LIFE EASIER — THEY MAKE LIFE MORE HARASSED.

SIX MINUTES TO MICROWAVE THIS?! WHO'S GOT THAT KIND OF TIME?!

IF WE WANTED MORE LEISURE, WE'D INVENT MACHINES THAT DO THINGS *LESS* EFFICIENTLY.

CALVIN and HOBBES

by WATTERSON

My mom and my dad are not what they seem.
Their dull appearance is part of their scheme.
I know of their plans. I know their techniques.
My parents are outer space alien freaks!

They landed on Earth in spaceships humongous.
Posing as grownups, they now walk among us.
My parents deny this, but I know the truth.
They're here to enslave me and spoil my youth.

Early each morning, as the sun rises,
Mom and Dad put on their earthling disguises.
I knew right away their masks weren't legit.
Their faces are lined – they sag and don't fit.

The Earth's gravity makes them sluggish and slow.
They say not to run, wherever I go.
They live by the clock. They're slaves to routines.
They work the year 'round. They're almost machines.

They deny that TV and fried food have much worth.
They cannot be human. They're not of this earth.
I cannot escape their alien gaze,
And they're warping my mind with their alien ways.
For sinister plots, this one is a gem.
They're bringing me up to turn *me* into *them!*

I'M FILLING OUT A READER SURVEY FOR *CHEWING* MAGAZINE.

SEE, THEY ASKED HOW MUCH MONEY I SPEND ON GUM EACH WEEK, SO I WROTE, "$500." FOR MY AGE, I PUT "43", AND WHEN THEY ASKED WHAT MY FAVORITE FLAVOR IS, I WROTE "GARLIC / CURRY."

THIS MAGAZINE SHOULD HAVE SOME AMUSING ADS SOON.

I LOVE MESSING WITH DATA.

EVER NOTICE HOW PEOPLE ALWAYS TRY TO DO TWO THINGS AT ONCE?

THEY TALK ON THE PHONE WHILE THEY DRIVE, THEY WATCH TV WHILE THEY EAT, THEY LISTEN TO MUSIC WHILE THEY WORK...

PEOPLE NEVER FOCUS ON ANY ONE THING TO ENJOY IT OR DO IT WELL.

YOU'RE BREAKING MY CONCENTRATION.

WE FOCUS ON DOING NOTHING AT ALL!

CALVIN AND HOBBES by WATTERSON

LOOK! A QUARTER!!

WOW! I'M RICH BEYOND MY DREAMS! I CAN HAVE ANYTHING I WANT! ALL MY PRAYERS HAVE BEEN ANSWERED!

MAYBE THERE'S MORE.

I'D BUILD A RAFT FOR THIS POND, BUT I DON'T HAVE A PLACE TO DOCK IT.

I'VE ALWAYS SAID YOU'RE A FRIEND WITHOUT PIER.

HUH?

NOTHING.

MM.

I GUESS YOU'RE UNDER A LOT OF PIER PRESSURE.

IS SOMETHING WRONG WITH YOU?!

HERE'S STINKY, THE TALKING SOCK! HI, STINKY! SAY SOMETHING TO SUSIE!

HELLO, YOU UGLY BUCKET OF BOOGERS!

THAT DARN "THROW YOUR VOICE" AD MADE IT SOUND LIKE EVERYONE WOULD BE FOOLED.

THERE AREN'T MANY HEROES THESE DAYS.

WHO IS OUT THERE TO INSPIRE US WITH A PERSONAL EXAMPLE OF VIRTUE AND SELF-SACRIFICE IN THE NAME OF A HIGHER GOOD?

WHO CAN WE LOOK UP TO? BUSINESS LEADERS? SPORTS FIGURES? POLITICIANS? CELEBRITIES? HECK, WE'RE LUCKY IF THEY DON'T END UP IN PRISON!

FORTUNATELY, IF WE CAN'T GET INSPIRATION, WE'LL ACCEPT ENTERTAINMENT.

AS USUAL, THE HERO BUSINESS IS UP TO ME.

OTHER KIDS' GAMES ARE ALL SUCH A BORE!
THEY'VE GOTTA HAVE RULES AND THEY GOTTA KEEP SCORE!
CALVINBALL IS BETTER BY FAR!
IT'S NEVER THE SAME! IT'S ALWAYS BIZARRE!
YOU DON'T NEED A TEAM OR A REFEREE!
YOU KNOW THAT IT'S GREAT, 'CAUSE IT'S NAMED AFTER ME!
IF YOU WANNA...

UH, FEEL FREE TO HARMONIZE WITH HOBBES ON THE RUMMA TUM TUMS.

THIS WAS A MISTAKE.

I'VE GOT THE CALVINBALL! EVERYBODY ELSE HAS TO GO IN SLOW MOTION NOW!

WAIT A MINUTE, CALVIN. I DON'T...

YOU HAVE TO *TALK* IN SLOW MOTION TOO. LIIIKE THISSS.

THIISSS GAAAAME MAAAKES NOOOO SENNNSE! IT'SSSS ΛΛSSS IFFFF YOU'RRRRE MAAAKINNNGGG IIIIIT UUUUP AAAS YOUUU GOOO.

HOBBES! SHE STUMBLED INTO THE PERIMETER OF WISDOM! RUN !!

OH...

CALVIN and HOBBES
by WATTERSON

THE BIG, STUPID ULTRASAUR TAKES A LONG DRINK...

.. A *VERY* LONG DRINK!

THE FEROCIOUS ALLOSAUR IS THIRSTY TOO! THIS MEANS CONFRONTATION!

..AH HEH HEH..

FORTUNATELY, THIS ALLOSAUR IS THE PATIENT TYPE.

Don't make me smack you across the hall, twerp.

WAKE UP! IT'S TIME TO GET READY FOR SCHOOL.

UHNGGG

JUST CHECKING. I'M GLAD YOU'RE UP AND DRESSED.

THAT SHOULD THROW HER OFF THE TRAIL FOR A WHILE.

FOR SHOW AND TELL, I BROUGHT A LITTLE TOY AIRPLANE.

IT'S SORT OF ORDINARY, I SUPPOSE, BUT I LIKE TO HAVE IT AROUND.

IT REMINDS ME THAT AS SOON AS I SAVE A LITTLE MORE MONEY, I'LL BUY A TICKET AND PUT SO MUCH DISTANCE BETWEEN YOU CHUMPS AND ME, IT WILL BOGGLE YOUR MINDS!

IT'S NOT AN "ATTITUDE," IT'S A *FACT!*

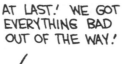

"ORIGINAL FLAVOR"... WAIT, HERE'S "LESS SODIUM," AND HERE'S "LITE," AND HERE'S "LESS FAT."

WHAT IF I WANT LESS FAT *AND* LESS SALT? WHAT DISTINGUISHES "LITE" FROM THESE OTHERS? DOES THE "ORIGINAL FLAVOR" PACKAGE IMPLY THAT THE OTHERS TASTE DIFFERENT?

FRANKLY, MY LIFE WAS PLENTY COMPLICATED *BEFORE* THE POTATO CHIPS.

LOOK AT ALL THIS PEANUT BUTTER! THERE MUST BE THREE SIZES OF FIVE BRANDS OF FOUR CONSISTENCIES! WHO DEMANDS THIS MUCH CHOICE??

I KNOW! I'LL QUIT MY JOB AND DEVOTE MY LIFE TO CHOOSING PEANUT BUTTER! IS "CHUNKY" CHUNKY ENOUGH, OR DO I NEED "*EXTRA* CHUNKY"?

I'LL COMPARE INGREDIENTS! I'LL COMPARE BRANDS! I'LL COMPARE SIZES AND PRICES! MAYBE I'LL DRIVE AROUND AND SEE WHAT *OTHER* STORES HAVE! SO MUCH SELECTION AND SO LITTLE TIME!

I THINK *YOU* SHOULD DO THE SHOPPING

DID THE MANAGER HAVE TO TALK TO YOU AGAIN?

HEY, WHERE'S THE PEANUT BUTTER?!

108

109

AND SO, AFTER A THREE MINUTE DOWNPOUR, HE BECAME LUDICROUSLY ATTIRED FOR THE REST OF THE DAY.

NOT EVERYONE CAN GET A FULL ISOMETRIC WORKOUT JUST BY YAWNING.

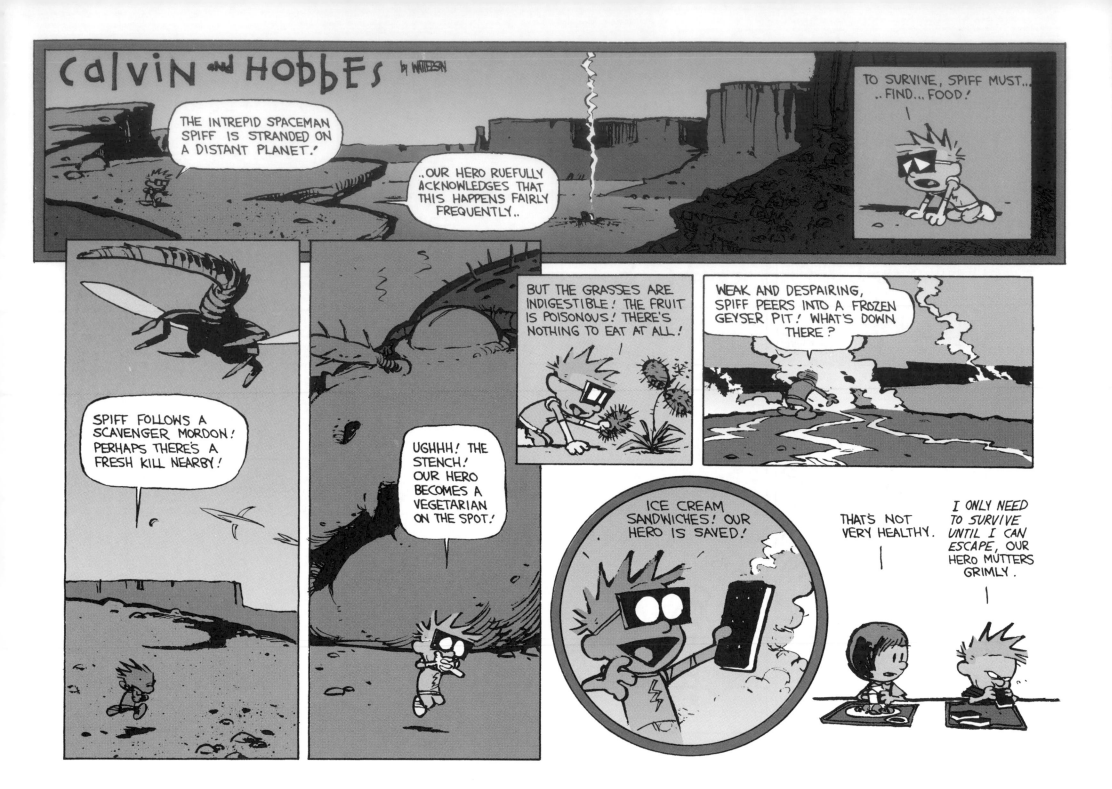

112

I WISH SCHOOL WOULD DISAPPEAR FOREVER, RIGHT NOW!

TO MAKE A BAD DAY WORSE, SPEND IT WISHING FOR THE IMPOSSIBLE.

UH OH, I FEEL A SNEEZE COMING ON.

AAA! NO TISSUE! NO HANKY! I.. AH.. AH... AH..

KACHOO!

OF MY LIMITED OPTIONS, THIS WAS PROBABLY THE WORST.

BOY, I HATE SCHOOL ASSIGNMENTS! MISS WORMWOOD IS OUT TO DESTROY MY LIFE!

WHAT DO YOU HAVE TO DO?

MAKE A LEAF COLLECTION! WHAT A DUMB WASTE OF TIME!

HOW MANY LEAVES DO YOU NEED?

50! I GOTTA COLLECT 50 LEAVES!

AND JUST WHEN I THOUGHT OF A LOOPHOLE, THE TEACHER SAID EVERY LEAF HAS TO BE A DIFFERENT KIND.

SHE'S GOT YOUR NUMBER.

WHEN DO YOU NEED TO PRESENT YOUR LEAF COLLECTION?

IN TWO WEEKS.

THAT'S NOT SO BAD. YOU JUST NEED THREE OR FOUR LEAVES A DAY.

I'M NOT WORKING ON WEEKENDS.

OK, FIVE LEAVES A DAY.

AND MY WEEKDAYS ARE BOOKED UNTIL NEXT THURSDAY AT 6 PM!

SO YOU NEED 50 LEAVES AN HOUR.

SEE?? IT'S IMPOSSIBLE!

OUR LEAF COLLECTIONS AREN'T DUE FOR A WEEK YET! HOW COULD YOU POSSIBLY BE ALMOST DONE ?!

I MAKE IT A GAME. I PRETEND IT'S A CONTEST TO SEE HOW MANY LEAVES I CAN FIND EACH DAY. THAT WAY, IT'S NOT AN ASSIGNMENT, IT'S FUN!

DID YOU KNOW THAT'S ONE OF THE TEN WARNING SIGNS OF HOPELESS DWEEBISM?

I'LL BET ANOTHER SIGN IS MOVING TO THE NEXT GRADE EACH YEAR.

THE TEACHER REMINDED US THAT WE ONLY HAVE A WEEK LEFT TO FINISH OUR LEAF COLLECTIONS, SO WE OUGHT TO BE HALF DONE NOW.

YOU HAVEN'T EVEN STARTED.

YEAH, BUT I WORK BETTER UNDER PRESSURE.

ACTUALLY, YOU WORK *ONLY* UNDER PRESSURE.

THAT WAY, THE WORK TIME IS MORE MISERABLE, BUT THERE'S LESS OF IT.

BOY, YOU LOOK TIRED. I'LL BET YOU WERE UP LATE DOING YOUR LEAF COLLECTION.

MAYBE, BUT *I'VE* GOT THE BEST COLLECTION OF ALL! *MY* LEAVES ARE FROM ANOTHER PLANET!

WHAT?!

SEE HOW BIZARRE THEY ARE? THE LABELS ARE EVEN WRITTEN IN AN ALIEN LANGUAGE! LOOK AT THEIR COOL ALPHABET!

IT LOOKS LIKE YOU TOOK 50 MAPLE LEAVES AND CUT THEM INTO WEIRD SHAPES.

ALIENS NOW OWN THE EARTH AND I TOLD THEM GIRLS MAKE GOOD ZOO EXHIBITS.

THE TEACHER DIDN'T BELIEVE MY LEAVES WERE FROM AN ALIEN PLANET.

SHE SAID IT WAS OBVIOUS I DID THE WHOLE THING LAST NIGHT AND I MADE A MOCKERY OF THE ASSIGNMENT. WELL, SHE'LL BE SORRY WHEN THE ALIENS SEND HER TO THE PLUTONIUM MINES.

SHE JUST WON'T ADMIT IT WAS A POINTLESS PROJECT. WHO CARES ABOUT LEAVES?! WHAT USELESS KNOWLEDGE!

I BELIEVE THAT'S POISON SUMAC YOU'RE HOLDING.

THIS?? WHAT MAKES YOU SAY THAT?

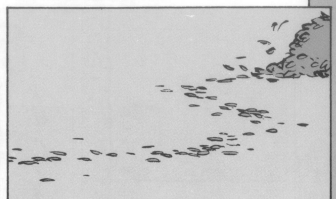

YOU KNOW, SCHOOL WOULDN'T BE SO BAD IF YOU DIDN'T HAVE TO GO EVERY DAY.

...AND IF YOU DIDN'T HAVE TO LEARN ANYTHING... AND IF YOU TOOK AWAY ALL THE TEACHERS AND ALL THE OTHER KIDS. IF IT WAS COMPLETELY DIFFERENT, SCHOOL WOULD BE GREAT.

A LOT OF THINGS ARE LIKE THAT.

NOBODY ASKS ME HOW THINGS OUGHT TO BE. I'VE GOT TONS OF IDEAS!

YES, CALVIN?

HEY KIDS, ON TOMORROW'S SHOW AND TELL, I'LL BE BRINGING A BIG SURPRISE! WILL IT SHOCK AND AMAZE YOU... *OR* WILL IT DISGUST AND TERRIFY YOU?? FIND OUT TOMORROW WHEN I REVEAL MY NEXT *SHOW AND TELL* HORROR! DON'T MISS IT!

RETURNING TO THE *LESSON*...

THAT'S CALLED A TEASER, BY THE WAY.

IN THE FUTURE, EVERYTHING WILL BE EFFORTLESS!

COMPUTERS WILL TAKE CARE OF EVERY TASK. WE'LL JUST POINT TO WHAT WE WANT DONE AND CLICK. WE'LL NEVER NEED TO LEAVE THE CLIMATE-CONTROLLED COMFORT OF OUR HOMES!

NO NUISANCE, NO WASTED TIME, NO ANNOYING HUMAN INTERACTION...

...NO LIFE.

LIFE IS TOO INCONVENIENT.

YOU'RE GOING TO JUGGLE EGGS?

IT'S A METAPHOR FOR LIFE, HOBBES.

EACH EGG REPRESENTS ONE OF LIFE'S CONCERNS AND THE GOAL IS TO GIVE EACH THE APPROPRIATE AMOUNT OF INDIVIDUAL ATTENTION WHILE SIMULTANEOUSLY WATCHING AND GUIDING ALL THE OTHERS.

LIFE IS ABOUT BALANCE AND STAYING QUICK AND ALERT AS EVERYTHING THREATENS TO SPIN OUT OF CONTROL!

AND SOMETIMES WE MAKE A BIG MESS OF THINGS.

BUT THE IMPORTANT THING IS PERSISTENCE.

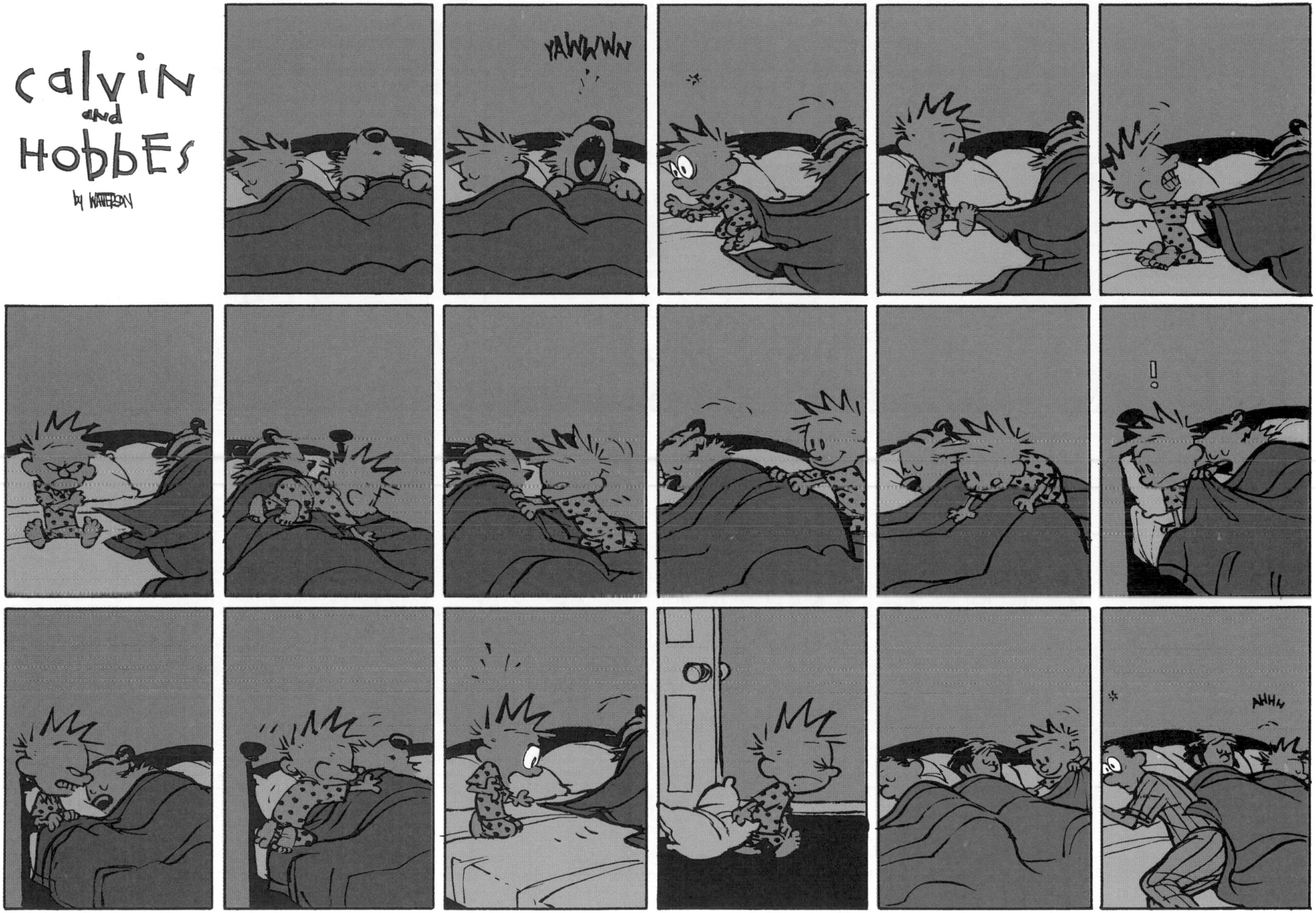
Calvin and Hobbes
by WATTERSON
YAWWWN
!
AHHH

WHY ISN'T MY LIFE LIKE THIS SITUATION COMEDY?

WHY DON'T I HAVE A BUNCH OF FRIENDS WITH NOTHING TO DO BUT DROP BY AND INSTIGATE WACKY ADVENTURES?

WHY AREN'T MY CONVERSATIONS PEPPERED WITH SPONTANEOUS WITTICISMS? WHY DON'T MY FRIENDS DEMONSTRATE HEARTFELT CONCERN FOR MY WELL-BEING WHEN I HAVE PROBLEMS?

WHY DON'T YOU KNOW ANY GORGEOUS BABES?

I GOTTA GET MY LIFE SOME WRITERS.

KNOW WHAT'S WEIRD? DAY BY DAY NOTHING SEEMS TO CHANGE, BUT PRETTY SOON, EVERYTHING IS DIFFERENT.

YOU JUST GO ABOUT YOUR BUSINESS AND ONE DAY YOU REALIZE YOU'RE NOT THE SAME PERSON YOU USED TO BE. PEOPLE CHANGE WHETHER THEY DECIDE TO OR NOT!

THANK HEAVEN FOR SMALL FAVORS.

FOR EXAMPLE, I USED TO BE MORE TOLERANT OF OBLIQUE ASPERSIONS.

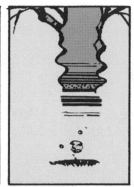

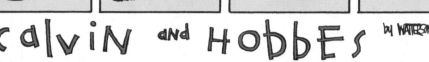

AS A GENIUS, IT'S IMPORTANT THAT I WRITE A LOT OF LETTERS.

AFTER ALL, MY CORRESPONDENCE WILL BE THE BASIC RESOURCE MATERIAL FOR HISTORIANS TO RECONSTRUCT MY LIFE. MY WRITING WILL PROVIDE COUNTLESS FASCINATING INSIGHTS FOR BIOGRAPHERS.

SUCH AS HOW ALL YOUR SALUTATIONS BEGIN, "HEY BOOGERBRAIN."

IT'S BEEN THREE WEEKS AND I STILL HAVEN'T RECEIVED MY X-RAY GLASSES!

YIKES! NOT ANOTHER EXTREME CLOSE-UP ON SOMEBODY'S ANGUISH AND GRIEF!

WHY DO TV CAMERAS ZOOM IN SO CLOSE TO PEOPLE'S FACES THAT YOU CAN'T EVEN SEE THEIR ENTIRE HEADS?! DO THEY THINK WE CAN'T READ THE PERSON'S EXPRESSION FROM MORE THAN TWO INCHES AWAY?!

WHAT A VIOLATION OF PERSONAL SPACE! WHAT A SHAMELESS INTRUSION! WHAT A HEARTLESS ASSAULT ON HUMAN DIGNITY!

WHY ARE YOU STANDING AGAINST THE WALL?

I'M WATCHING TV.

AUGHH! THIS STUPID TOASTER BURNED MY TOAST!!

LOOK AT THIS! MY TOAST IS CHARRED TO A BLACK CINDER! I CAN'T EAT THIS! IT'S RUINED! *RUINED!!*

SO STICK IN ANOTHER PIECE OF BREAD AND WATCH IT THIS TIME.

ARE YOU SUGGESTING THAT THIS APPLIANCE DIDN'T AGGRAVATE ME WITH MALICE AFORETHOUGHT?!

I KEEP HAVING THE SAME WEIRD DREAM EVERY NIGHT.

IF IT'S THE SAME DREAM, IT MUST *MEAN* SOMETHING.

I THINK IT MEANS THE FALL SEASON FLOPPED AND MY SUBCONSCIOUS WENT INTO RERUNS.

BRRR, IT'S FREEZING OUT THERE! I DON'T WANT TO LEAVE MY NICE WARM BED.

ON DAYS LIKE THIS, I WISH MOM WOULD COME IN, LAY AN EXTRA BLANKET OVER ME, PAT MY HEAD, AND AS I SINK INTO THE PILLOW UNDER THE WEIGHT OF THE COVERS, SHE'D SAY...

HEY, LET'S *MOVE* IT!! THIS IS THE THIRD TIME I'VE CALLED YOU! YOU'RE GOING TO MISS THE BUS! *LET'S GO!!*

THESE MORNINGS ARE GOING TO KILL ME.

THE PACE OF MODERN LIFE IS ALL WRONG. IT MAKES EVERY DAY AN ORDEAL. EVERYBODY'S EXHAUSTED, STRESSED OUT, AND SHORT-TEMPERED!

LOOK AT ME! WHY AM I WAITING FOR A BUS AT THIS HORRIBLE HOUR?! IT'S UNNATURAL AND UNHEALTHY!

WE SHOULD *EASE* INTO THE DAY! YOU KNOW, READ THE PAPER, HAVE SOME HOT COCOA, GO FOR A LEISURELY WALK AND GET OUR THOUGHTS TOGETHER...

SO NOW IT'S MID-AFTERNOON.

RIGHT. TIME TO KICK BACK FOR A LITTLE SIESTA AND PLAN DINNER.

THIS IS A PHOTOGRAPH OF ME WHEN I WAS TWO.

IT'S STRANGE. I *KNOW* THAT'S ME, BUT I DON'T FEEL ANY CONNECTION TO THIS IMAGE. EVERYTHING IS SO DIFFERENT NOW.

ISN'T IT WEIRD THAT ONE'S OWN PAST CAN SEEM UNREAL? THIS IS LIKE LOOKING AT A PICTURE OF SOMEBODY ELSE.

SAY, A SLOBBERING NUDIST WITH LEGS LIKE LINK SAUSAGES.

YOU KNOW, NOW I CAN'T *STAND* TO WAD A SOGGY BLANKET IN MY MOUTH.

HERE'S A PICTURE OF ME WHEN I WAS THREE. LOOK AT THAT SMILE!

AHH, THE ARROGANCE OF YOUTH! I THOUGHT I KNEW EVERYTHING WHEN I WAS THREE.

AND YOU EXPWETHED AWW THAT KNOWWEDGE WIKE THITH.

NOW, A LIFETIME OF EXPERIENCE HAS LEFT ME BITTER AND CYNICAL.

OOH, IT'S COLD TODAY! IT NEEDS TO BE 30 DEGREES WARMER OUT HERE!

FOR THAT MATTER, IT'S ALSO TOO QUIET. WE NEED SOME BACKGROUND MUSIC.

AND IT'S TOO SLOW! THINGS SHOULD HAPPEN MORE QUICKLY!

IF ONLY BEING OUTSIDE WERE MORE LIKE DRIVING A CAR.

YEAH, I COULD BE SITTING DOWN NOW TOO.

CALVIN, WILL YOU GATHER THE TRASH, PLEASE?

WHY SHOULD I? WHAT DO I GET IN RETURN?!

WE WILL FEED, CLOTHE, SHELTER, AND EDUCATE YOU THROUGHOUT YOUR ENTIRE YOUTH.

I REALLY HATE HAVING THINGS PUT IN PERSPECTIVE.

calviN and HObbEs by WATTERSON

EVER NOTICE HOW MANY CONVERSATIONS REVOLVE AROUND TV SHOWS AND MOVIES?

OUR COMMON REFERENCES ARE EVENTS THAT NEVER HAPPENED AND PEOPLE WE'LL NEVER MEET! WE KNOW MORE ABOUT CELEBRITIES AND FICTIONAL CHARACTERS THAN WE KNOW ABOUT OUR NEIGHBORS!

THAT MUST BE WHY NEW HOUSES AREN'T BUILT WITH BIG FRONT PORCHES ANYMORE.

I CAN'T BELIEVE DAD WON'T LET ME HAVE A TV IN MY OWN ROOM.

I LIKE THE SOUND OF SLEET HITTING THE WINDOW PANES AT NIGHT.

AND I LIKE WHEN THE SLEET TURNS TO HEAVY SNOW AS IT GETS COLDER, SO YOU KNOW THAT TOMORROW THE WORLD WILL BE BURIED IN ICE AND SNOW!

IT'S ONE OF THE FEW PLEASURES RESERVED FOR THOSE WHO DON'T DRIVE.

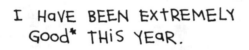

157

THE CHRISTMAS SEASON IS ALWAYS A TIME FOR PERSONAL REFLECTION.

TOO OFTEN, WE DON'T EXAMINE OUR LIVES. THIS IS A TIME TO TAKE STOCK AND THINK ABOUT WHAT'S IMPORTANT.

IT'S A TIME TO REDEDICATE ONESELF TO FRENZIED ACQUISITION..., A TIME TO SPREAD THE JOY OF MATERIAL WEALTH... A TIME TO GLORIFY PERSONAL EXCESS OF EVERY KIND!

EARTHLY REWARDS MAKE CONSUMERISM A POPULAR RELIGION.

...A TIME TO ATONE FOR ONE'S FRUGALITY!

OH BOY, LOOK AT ALL THE SNOW! IT MUST BE SIX INCHES DEEP!

THIS WILL BE PERFECT FOR SLEDDING OR...

DING DONG

DING DONG DING DONG

ALL RIGHT! I'M COMING! I'M COMING!

WHAT THE HECK IS WRONG WITH THIS PLANET YOU SOLD US?!

THE NEW ISSUE OF *CHEWING* TELLS HOW TO STAY IN TOP CHEWING CONDITION OVER THE WINTER!

WHAT'S SO HARD ABOUT THAT? YOU CAN CHEW GUM ALL YEAR.

WE SERIOUS CHEWERS NEED A LOT MORE THAN STRONG JAW MUSCLES, YOU KNOW! TO CHEW HOUR AFTER HOUR, WE NEED A TOTAL CROSS-TRAINING FITNESS REGIME!

SO THE IDEA IS TO INCREASE THE AMOUNT OF THIS HOBBY YOU CAN ENDURE.

RIGHT. WHEN YOU'RE GOOD AT IT, IT'S REALLY MISERABLE.

SOMETIMES AT NIGHT I WORRY ABOUT THINGS AND THEN I CAN'T FALL ASLEEP.

IN THE DARK, IT'S EASIER TO IMAGINE AWFUL POSSIBILITIES THAT YOU'D NEVER BE PREPARED FOR.

AND IT'S HARD TO FEEL COURAGEOUS IN LOOSE-FITTING, DROWSY BEAR JAMMIES.

THAT'S WHY TIGERS SLEEP IN THE BUFF!

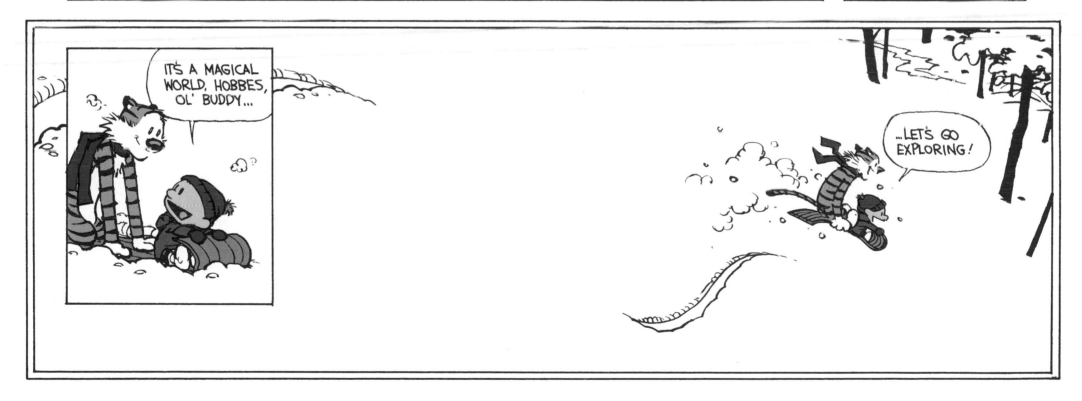